TRAINING LOG BOOK

Rob Pincus

I.C.E. Publishing Company
Contributing Editor: Nancy Clark
Illustrations & Cover Design: Oleg Volk

Library of Congress Control Number: 2008908001

ISBN 13: 978-0-9791508-3-8

Printed in USA.

For Our Students

Contents

Foreword 7

Introduction 11

Warrior Expert Theory 17

The Efficiency Principle 23

The Plausibility Principle 29

Contributions 33

- Michael Bane 35
- Steve Barron 37
- Tony Blauer 39
- Frank Borelli 42
- John Brown 44
- Paul Castle 46
- John Chapman 47
- Wes Doss 49
- Craig Douglas 51
- John S. Farnam 53
- Tom Givens 55
- Paul Haberstroh 57
- Denny Hansen 59
- Gila Hayes 62
- Marty Hayes 64

Michael Janich 66
Tiger McKee 68
Gary Meares 70
John Meyer 72
Peter Moll 74
Ken Murray 75
Kent O'Donnell 77
Tim O'Rourke 78
Troy Price 80
Tony Scotti 82
Clint Smith 84
Randy Smith 86
Robert Smith, M.D. 88
Dave Spaulding 90
Andy Stanford 92
Colin Tinnin 95
Mark Warren & Vaughn Baker 97
Claude Werner 100
James Yeager 102

Training Resources 105

INTEGRITY

CONSISTENCY

EFFICIENCY

Foreword

When Rob asked me to write a few lines about his new Log Book project, I thought, "It's about time somebody created one of these things." Many times I wish I would have had a book like this. Let's face it, we all have good intentions about documenting our training, but few of us have a decent system in place. As a pilot, I log every flight hour. Without it, it's impossible to obtain any sort of credit for the costly investment I have made advancing my aviation pursuits. As a skydiver, I have to keep a log of every jump. Lacking my Jump Log as proof of my experience, nobody would want to be party to the more advanced formations with me. I even keep a workout journal to track my personal progress in that area. Yet, for all of the training that I have done in various areas of the tactical arena, the only proof I have that the training actually occurred is often in the form of a certificate issued by the course leader. What about every shot that I've fired, or ten-minute dry firing session, or afternoon spent honing my tactical skills with friends while engaging each other with Airsoft? They are small but important pieces to the overall training puzzle, certainly. Until now, there's not been a formal Log Book in which to write this stuff down.

In my book "The Ten Minute Warrior®," I discuss the value of incremental training to overall proficiency levels in the various areas of training. Ten minutes each day equals more than sixty hours per year. It adds up quickly—from the article you read in a magazine dealing with Fourth Amendment issues to the half dozen draw strokes you perform prior to going on duty. These are all small, but important training increments on your way to higher levels of proficiency making it essential that you document every important step.

Following each and every use of force you deploy against Joe Citizen, you are required to articulate what you did and why you did it. In the event your actions are questioned in a court of law, the record of your training in the particular area in question will often be scrutinized by some plaintiff's attorney. "Just how often do you actually train to deploy your firearm, officer?" To be able to answer "Every day," and back that up with a professionally documented record, nicely punctuates the hard-won confidence in your abilities. Beyond that (much like a collection of personal journals over the years), it is truly gratifying to look back at where you were and demonstrate to yourself just how much work you've done and how much progress you have made. As humans, we build on our successes and take pride in our accomplishments. Although a few minutes a day doesn't seem like much, the ability to look back over a record of the past five years showing hundreds of hours of training can't help but instill the sense of pride you should have in that achievement.

Personally, I'm looking forward to starting the process of keeping a Log Book of my shooting and tactical training myself. It's long overdue. You've made the first important decision by purchasing this important book. Thanks for joining me in charting the training journey.

Ken Murray
Author, *Training at The Speed of Life*

Learn like you will live forever,
live like you will die tomorrow.
Ghandi

Introduction

I took my first formal defensive training course almost thirty years ago. It was a series of basic karate courses that were part of an activity program that our town offered during the summer school break. It wasn't much to speak of and I barely remember the details. That was probably the first place I learned to tie a proper knot in a gi belt and not much else came from it.

Since that summer, I've been through hundreds of blocks of instruction—in the military, police and private sector. The topics spanned from knife fighting to eavesdropping countermeasures to drill and ceremony with a lot of stops and rounds downrange in between. I can honestly report that there has always been something that made every course stand out as worthwhile, some being more valuable than others. Whether it was the information, the range time, the exercises, a new friend or business contact, seeing a new piece of equipment or learning something about myself or a teammate/partner, something good has always come from the training experience.

A couple of years ago, some members of the Swiss military enrolled in my Combat Focus Shooting course and asked me to sign their training log books at the end of the final day. The small hardcover book had page after page of courses logged in it. It reminded me a little of my old pilot logbook from the never completed flying lessons I took during high school. Every single training endeavor of their military careers was documented in those books, from a single hour spent learning how to properly use a gas mask to a four-week mountaineering course. How valuable was that? How many important lessons could they be reminded of just by flipping through the pages? How many important contacts existed on those pages as potential resources to help with problems or answer questions on the myriad of topics that they had been trained in over the years?

I was jealous.

Later that week, I started a log book of my own to document courses that I was teaching. I now have two books that I use for this purpose, one for the United States and one for Europe. I have students sign in and add comments. Often, I print class pictures and paste them in the book as well. These simple journals filled with blank pages, the kind available at any bookstore, served the basic purpose well. As I've had students sign my books, many of them have mentioned what a good idea it was and implied that they would start their own. I owe credit to my students over the years for a large percentage of information I include in my courses. Discussions with students, their inquiries, their experiences and their equipment have dictated much of the direction and development in the programs my staff instructors and I teach. My journals now include notes relevant to important discussions with students and adaptations to accommodate their equipment or context.

I don't get as much time to enroll in and attend courses as I would like anymore, but I enjoy sitting in on the courses at training conferences when I'm not teaching myself. Earlier this year, at the 1 Inch to 100 Yards Conference in Laughlin, Nevada, I finally committed to assembling this Training Log Book for others to use. Designing the pages to specifically make it easy to record the important aspects of training activities was a quick process. Together with some of my friends and associates at that event, I roughed out the important aspects the group determined would be essential to record: Topics, Locations, Instructors and Classmates. Over the next couple of months, I filled in other pieces of the puzzle: Was a certificate issued? What equipment was used or purchased during the event?

As the Log Book project got closer to completion, I realized that it offered me the opportunity to share some basic information related to training of any kind. That in mind, I recruited some friends to contribute their thoughts and advice to the

Log Book, addressing what prospective students are seeking, considerations they may have in participating in or evaluating a training course. My friends' cumulative advice and insight is drawn from decades of participating in both sides of the classroom. Originally, the plan was to have about 20 to 30 pages of content. The volume that you are now reading contains over 100 pages of information provided by top instructors from around the industry! Over the course of the project, I obviously invited more than just a few friends and, thankfully, over 90% of those invited (many under a tight deadline for production) graciously agreed to offer their advice. It's advice that's worth reading more than once.

The most important piece of advice that I can give you when it comes to training is to simply go out and do it. Take advantage of any opportunity to learn from your instructors, peers or students.

Train well and train often.

Rob Pincus

The Athletic Ability to draw fast and shoot straight is not nearly as important as the ability to recognize an attack as early as possible and respond efficiently and appropriately given the environment, training and tools available.

-RJP

Warrior Expert Theory

The more frequently and realistically you train, the more likely you will be to recognize what is happening and what you need to do during a dynamic critical incident. Warrior Expert Theory is a quantifiable concept. Experts respond to information differently than laymen. Following extensive study, a person can learn to *recognize* patterns of information instead of attempting to sort through the individual parts in an attempt to compute how they relate to one another. With practice, an individual can learn to perform complex tasks like drawing a firearm from a concealed holster and firing rounds into a target without working through a conscious cognitive thought process weighing each step along the way.

Recognition is a powerful tool the brain uses to relate to information it has been exposed to previously. Most commonly, we consider recognition something we use to relate to people. Imagine showing up early to a training course to find two other students at the range. Say the student to the left is someone you worked with until he made the move to new employment. You recall that his wife had been hospitalized after an illness and that their daughter recently started college. You know nothing about the person to the right, but it just so happens that you learn he also recently started a new job, dropped his daughter off at college and picked his wife up from the hospital after an illness. You could say the same three sentences to either person: "How's your wife doing?" "Is your daughter enjoying her first semester at college?" "How is the new job going?" Your conversation could be highly efficient using only those three questions if you go left. If you ask questions to the right, however, you will probably have to engage in a rather lengthy exchange and establish a level of trust before you can reasonably and appropriately pose those questions to a stranger. It would take more time, effort and energy to have that conversation with a stranger because you don't *recognize* what to say immediately. Your previous exposure to information about the fellow student to the left expedites your goal of having a meaningful conversation.

This some process applies to learning how attacks develop, the pre-attack cues you can pick up on to avoid or preempt a threat, how your firearm works, how to most conveniently carry a firearm for defense, how it feels to get hit, how it feels to strike someone with an elbow and all the other countless hundreds pieces and parts of information and experiences you stand to gather during your training. Learning to recognize the fragments of information and the patterns they represent, as well as putting pieces together to form an efficient response, is what becoming a Warrior Expert entails.

Exposure can assume many forms. You can gather information by reading a book, an article or even a post on an Internet forum. Watch a training DVD or a dash camera recording or witness experienced students performing exercises to glean telling data. Formal training courses, informal shooting sessions and even competitive shooting events can provide a wealth of information. Seek out the important pieces that are relevant to you and further refine them based on the most solid foundations and assumptions you can make. Findings derived from sources similar to issues aligned with your own, particularly when you've applied reasoning and sound methodology while assessing solutions are optimum. Individuals who have already walked through resolving similar issues can also have a lot to offer. Peers developing their own Warrior Expertise can contribute to your data gathering process, too, by asking appropriate questions and sharing training regimens they've applied successfully in the past. When you get down to it, sources of information are nearly pervasive. Of course, you need to filter the collected information with a skeptical and discerning eye. As you become more sensitized to patterns, you likewise will become more proficient at sorting and prioritizing data, you're likely to hone in on the pieces that are particularly appropriate to you.

Identify which threats have the highest probability of occurring to you in your lifetime. Weigh this in the context of a potential dynamic critical incident. The answers will help define the amount of time you will need to invest in training to deal with these immediate concerns. The process will never stop; it will just become more refined.

The more realistically and frequently you train, the faster you will move along your path to becoming a Warrior Expert. Don't set your sights too short. For true professionals and the most serious students of self-defense, the path will never end. Your realistic goal should be to become expert enough to deal with your next threat… a situation level you can never predict. Push to become more knowledgeable, more skilled and better prepared.

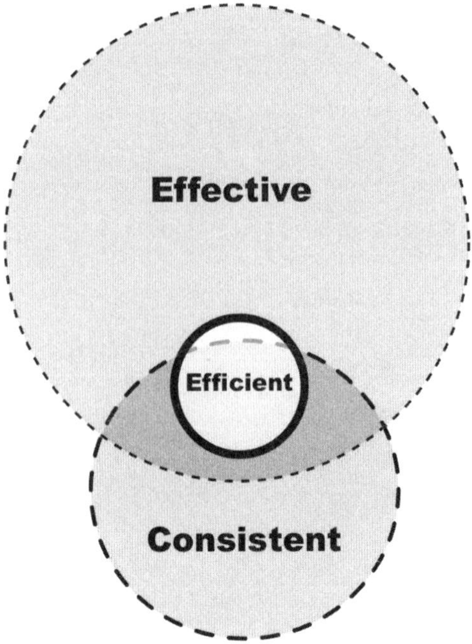
Effective
Efficient
Consistent

The Efficiency Principle

Find ways to achieve your goals with as little time effort and energy as possible.

When you are evaluating a technique to determine its validity, you can use the Efficiency Principle to make the job easier. There are a lot of techniques that would be classified as effective, but the fact that some technique or tactic would be effective alone under some set of circumstances is not enough justification to make it a part of your training regimen. Simply achieving a goal, such as hitting the target or reloading the gun is not nearly enough to legitimize the use of a technique. If you think of all the possible ways in which someone could reload a semi-automatic pistol, you would quickly realize that simply getting from empty to loaded is does not mean that you are doing it as efficiently as possible. Achieving a goal with as little time, effort and mental energy as possible is a good definition of efficiency. Using this definition, you can objectively evaluate any technique in the context of your most likely scenario to determine whether or not it is the most efficient option. If you are new to defensive training and you have only one option that works, train it. As soon as you start learning about the options, start evaluating to determine which is most efficient. Keep in mind the context that you are training for. You can use the Plausibility Principle (see Page 28) to weed out many techniques that are designed for situations and circumstances that aren't likely to apply to you. If you are an CCW permit holder interested in training for self defense, techniques developed for sport shooting or for a tactical team environment wouldn't meet the Plausibility Test, for example.

While you are evaluating the plausible techniques, be sure to give extra attention to those techniques that seem like they would be most efficient (ie- require less time, effort and mental energy) during a *worst-case scenario*. The worst-case scenario doesn't mean you against a platoon of marines with a Lorcin .380. It means a *plausible* situation in which you are caught off guard but survive the initial ambush and need to effect the situation as efficiently as possible. Does a reloading technique require looking at the pistol? Does your shooting technique require a specific stance? Does your shooting position assume two hands on the gun? As it is plausible that your situation would not allow those things, the techniques would be suspect in terms of their true efficiency in context.

It is important to draw a clear distinction between things that you find "easy" or that you can do "fast" and things that are objectively efficient in the context that you will need them. Fast and Easy are subjective terms that are heavily influenced by your experience and situation. If you are standing on a square range, not under stress, on a well lit day with nothing to think about except for shooting and reloading, you may find some very inefficient things to be *fast and easy*. As you've probably heard before: Be careful what you practice, you may get really good at the wrong thing.

Another term that it is important to understand is consistency. The vast majority of the time, the things that you will ultimately find to be efficient will also be consistent with other things that you do and certainly be consistent with the context of your most likely situations. Don't let yourself focus exclusively on consistency. Clinging to one facet of a technique or tactic (always looking at the front sight when you pres s the trigger or the first man through the door always going left, for example) may not be effective in certain situations. That said, however, doing things the same way and in the same place/position as often as possible will increase your efficiency. Limiting the options that you practice will also increase consistency and tend to increase your efficiency the majority of the time.

The diagram on Page 21 shows the relationship between Effectiveness, Consistency and Efficiency. In order to be efficient, something must be effective first. The majority of the time you will find that consistency is a contributing factor to efficiency.

Keep the efficiency principle in the forefront of your mind when evaluating, choosing and developing your skills.

The Plausibility Principle is an important fundamental concept that should help you to sift through the incredible amount of information available in the world of self-defense, firearms and tactical training. The Plausibility Principle can also help you manage your valuable, and limited, training resources: time, effort and budget.

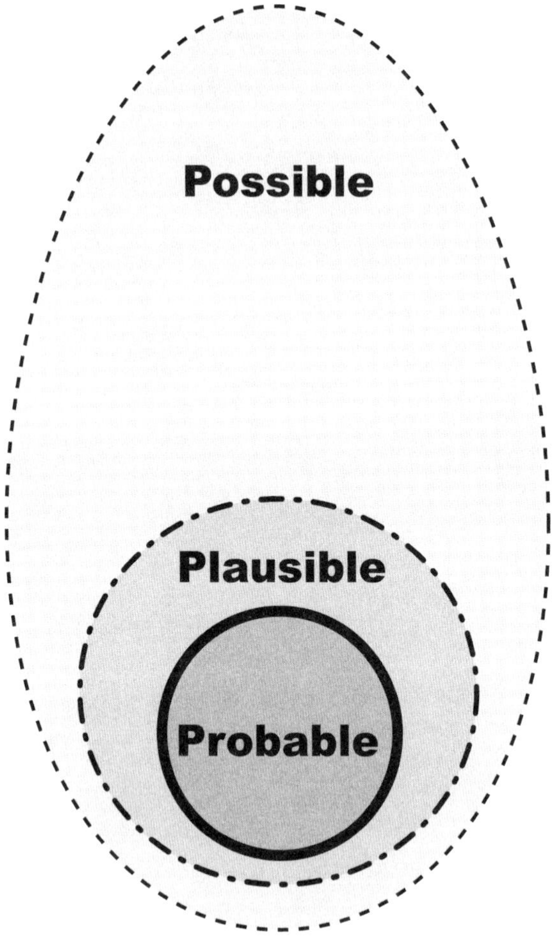
Possible
Plausible
Probable

The Plausibility Principle

Spend your limited resources appropriately, relative to the likelihood of gaining useful value.

One the one hand, there isn't a legitimate school that is teaching for scenarios that aren't possible or teaching techniques that aren't effective. On the other, there isn't a person on the planet that has enough time, money or energy to learn all the possible techniques that they might need for all of the possible situations that those schools can come up with. With this in mind, simply saying that something *could* happen or that a technique works under *some set* of circumstances isn't enough. The student needs to be skeptical of anything justified only by possibility.

Knowing that our training resources are limited,

we must prioritize what we prepare for and what we learn. It is intuitively true that we must spend most of our time preparing for what is most likely to happen and what is most likely to work under those circumstances. These are the things that are referred to as probable. What is probable for *you* varies with your environment, profession, equipment, athleticism and many other variables. The chances are good that with a little thought and research you can find out what the most likely defensive situations for you are going to be. Once you understand when you are most likely to need the skills you are developing, you can be a better judge of what skills you need to develop. Understanding which skills you need to develop allows you to prioritize your training time so that you spend most of the time, training for what is most likely to help. If you are most likely to encounter a close quarters attack, you're going to need to develop unarmed responses to go along with the use of your preferred defensive tool. If you are part of a military unit, you will most likely need to learn to use specific equipment, regardless of what you personally prefer.

After you have covered the situations considered probable, you can apply some of your training time to situations and techniques that are somewhat less likely to be needed, but which you still deem as reasonably appropriate areas in which to spend your training resources. These are the areas that fall within the scope of things that are plausible. Based on empirical evidence (experience of others, available statistics, physiology, human behavior, natural reactions, the way your equipment works, etc), trends in your environment, new training developments and a host of other information, you can make educated guesses about areas in which it is also appropriate to spend your time.

Once something reasonable has moved from plausible to probable, you are already behind the curve. Critically thinking about your situation and studying the empirical evidence will allow you to not only recognize what is obviously within the *probable* area, it will also help you determine the things that should fall within the almost as important *plausible* zone.

Employ your time in improving yourself by other men's writings so that you shall come easily by what others have labored hard for.

-Socrates

Contributions

The initial response from many professional instructors when I mentioned this project was one version or another of "great idea". The conversation that followed often included the fact that we all wish we had kept this kind of log book from the beginning and/or that many had mentioned logging training information to students in one way or another at various times. My question to these industry professionals became "What other advice do you have for anyone looking for, considering, attending or evaluating a defensive/ tactical training course?"

The following pages contain the responses from some of the top people in the industry who generously agreed to contribute to this work. All totaled, their wisdom represents over 300 years of professional training experience!

The intent is that you will revisit these pages often during your training process and use them as guidance, motivation and inspiration.

Michael Bane

Some firearms trainers exhibit an near-obsessive need to equate their firearms skills with street warrior cred, and in some instances backgrounds that perhaps existed only in online games rather than in the real world. As a friend (a SEAL) said last year, if everyone that claims to have been a SEAL had actually been a SEAL, SEAL reunions would have to rent the entire state of Nevada just to accommodate the crowds.

My absolute favorite training story hails from my sweetie's personal protection class a few years ago. She wanted to get her CCW and the class was a requirement, and as I hadn't sat in on a personal protection class in years I agreed to attend the class with her. The instructor walked into the class and said (I swear), "I can kill you with a gun. I can kill you with a bow. I can kill you with a pencil. And I can kill you with my bare hands." The rest of the class was every bit as good, involving a plethora of questionable techniques, profound misunderstandings about both firearms and firearms law, and a level of self-aggrandizement that would make Jean-Claude Van Damme blush.

Yeah, we all love war stories, and in truth, a lot

of such stories are exchanged over adult beverages after class. But one of my primary criteria for an instructor is minimal testosterone. I have met a lot of dangerous people, and not a one of them has gone out of his or her way to convince me that they are reputable instructors unless they pledge that they can teach me to stop an attack. What I want from a trainer is knowledge transfer. Sure, you might be able to kill me with a pencil or at least an Etch-A-Sketch, but unless you can teach me how to stop you from killing me with said implement, you don't deserve my money and I don't have the time to waste.

Training is either evolving or its worthless. As the world changes training needs to change. There are a lot of hide-bound firearms trainers out there. Oftentimes they cast their inability to evolve as "sticking to what has always worked." The best instructors are equally the best students, always learning and seeking opportunity to learn. Sensei learns from students as students learn from sensei.

Finally, be wary of trainers who put their names on every technique. It's sort of like having a vanity license plate that reads "Stud." Um, no, I think not. Finally, finally, have fun. You can be serious and still be joyful in your training. Heck, the world might not end after all, but you'll still be able to shoot!

Michael Bane
Host/Producer, ***Shooting Gallery***

Steve Barron

Developing and maintaining your skill as a combat shooter is a lifelong pursuit that never ends. To become proficient, you must focus your studies and training efforts on combat-proven methods. Shooting techniques must be simple in nature and compatible with the body's response to combat induced stress.

Select a firearm make and model that has a proven performance record in the real world. Stick with that weapon and work with it until its operation becomes second nature to you.

Train on a regular basis. Frequent training sessions firing only a few boxes of ammunition will yield better results than sporadic or infrequent sessions involving large expenditures of ammunition.

Remember, sub-caliber firearms are of value in developing and maintaining skills.

If possible, get involved in force-on-force training classes. Force-on-force training classes (if conducted properly) represent the upper-end of the training spectrum.

Do not neglect the issue of developing defensive skills other than the firearm.

Most defensive situations do not require deadly force. Make sure you have options other than the gun.

Never lose your focus on safety.

Steve Barron
Staff Instructor, Hocking College

Tony Blauer

Word to the Why's

No single course can possibly cover all aspects of tactical development. The only way to develop the total tactical toolbox is to train with multiple mentors over a period of time. Even if you could get access to all conceivable data at once, absorbing it would be a near impossibility. Yet you can make the most of your pursuit of training by keeping the following in mind:

Be tactical and practical with your course selection. Check the instructor's history and reverences. Get peer reviews—from other instructors, not just former students. And, of course, tap online resources as well.

Real fights happen in the space of a phone booth. Get some extreme close quarter, hand-to-hand training. Get off the 20 x 20 mat and into a bus and a bathroom. In other words, don't just train in fine spaces; train in confined spaces.

Put your training into practice. Coach Bear Bryant said, "The will to win compares little with the will to prepare to win." Make sure you are enacting scenarios in your practice.

Work the warrior as athlete (www.crossfit.com),

followed by working the warrior athlete as tactician (realistic scenario training). A huge missing link in most tactical training is tactical fitness. True preparedness comes down to fitness for fighting vs. fitness for fun.

Your gun is your secondary weapon; you are the primary weapon. Like the metaphor says: the weapon is an extension of the body/mind. Your skill with a firearm, knife, stick or improvised weapon will be directly proportional with how competent you are empty-handed. If you are the weapon, you are always armed.

Your mind navigates your muscles. Combat psychology and tactical mind-set development is vital. Remember, the weakest link in a tactical chain is the human factor. The objective is to achieve the 3-D model—integrating the emotional, psychological and physical toolbox.

A true warrior seeks weakness; not just in his enemy but also more importantly in himself. Don't restrict your attendance to courses promoting skills you already own. Follow your fear. Your course selections should not look like a Christmas wish list; rather, it should like a performance diet. What are the essential ingredients that will make you a more complete tactical warrior? What areas do you need to work on? Concentrate on your week areas in order to change your tactical presence (which incidentally is the first thing your opponent sees).

The decision to attend training should always be determined by the "why factor" not the "wow" factor. While the type of equipment or the promise of some dramatic FTX can be districting, it's not the number of courses you've attended that matters, but the quality of the coursework.

In the end, there is no single course that offers all the answers, tactics or training. Yet a proactive and thoughtful accumulation of training will enhance your capabilities and enhance survivability. Bottom line: look to courses that will improve your skills not fill your resume.

Tony Blauer
Blauer Tactical Systems

Frank Borelli

When we, in any martial profession, seek a school we usually tend to look for those with far greater experience than we see in ourselves. Yet when we look at the honored and revered trainers – those who have "been there and done that" we usually find trainers who are themselves constantly seeking some new tidbit of knowledge; some previously not experienced skill; SOMETHING new. The greatest instructors are those who never stop seeing themselves as students. That outlook – the willingness to learn at every turn; the desire to seek new knowledge and new skills from the least likely of sources as well as from the most honored places (i.e. boot camp or police academy) – that outlook is what is imperative for every contemporary warrior. If you're lucky it's something you learned as a child and maintained through to adulthood. If you're not so lucky it's either something you learned when you realized others had it *or it's time for you to learn it now.* In the post-9/11 America I believe that every citizen needs to embrace this outlook and train for the eventuality of another terrorist attack. If it never comes then we're no worse off. If it comes and we're not prepared then we are up the creek without a paddle… or a canoe for that matter. Never before has the saying, "If you want peace, prepare for war" been as true as it is today.

As others I'm sure have said: go into every training session with an open mind; a mind that is a sponge and a body that is willing to work. Sweat never hurt anyone. Work one up and figure out what you've learned that is worth keeping. Don't discard what you might not feel is of value but tuck it away for future evaluation. Most of all, never lose 1) the willingness to learn, and 2) the willingness to use your knowledge in defense of yourself and justice.

Frank Borelli
Newamericantruth.com

John Brown

As a young "Wanna Be" Frogman, my instructors filled my head with advice. "Keep your mouth shut, and ears open!" "Volunteer for every job, no matter how bad." "Never turn down a school," etcetera. And while all of these were important in "becoming" a sound operator, a lot of them went by the way side after a couple of years of experience. One of the pieces of advice that stayed with my however, was given to me in a class by Instructor Rich Clifford. He told us that we "should always keep and maintain a Breacher Book," or a training logbook. When I need to look back and find out what gear worked and what didn't, or what I would have liked to have had on a snowy night in the mountains of Virginia, I go to my training logbook. Keeping track of the round count, instructors, key points of the class and what information you found to be of the most value to you will allow you to go back and review or help you remember what your problem areas were, and thereby make yourself stronger at them. Without the ability to look back at where you are deficient, you have the potential of being less efficient in your training, which is, after all, the point of training in the first place.

I also think that it is very important to discuss physical training or physical readiness. As a trainer I have become acutely aware that the best chance that we have of surviving a dynamic critical incident is to be as prepared as possible both physically and mentally. To that end, various facets of the fitness industry have recognized the need for exercise programs that very closely resemble the demands of life, using movements that can be found in day to day occurrences in the lives of everyone, from the armed professional and the housewife alike. Through CrossFit's prescription of "Functional Movements, Constantly Varied and executed at High Intensity,", for example, we find the opportunity to make our bodies more readily accepting of the rigors of life. If you aren't taking care of these aspects in training as well, then you are not nearly as prepared as you think you are and more importantly, you may not be as prepared as you may *NEED* to be.

John Brown
I.C.E. Staff Instructor
Agoge Training

Paul Castle

In quality training, there will be challenge and, ultimately, self-realization. The test of a man in the fearful crucible of battle is no easy thing…nor should preparation for that test be easy. When one who intends to become capable of defending him or herself or others, the task at hand is not always clear. The skills and self control that are shaped in good training will enhance the ability to perform on demand. Many put their trust in luck, but luck can be good or bad. Good luck is prone to desert you when you need it most. It is my belief that the best luck is created when preparation meets opportunity.

Paul Castle
Sabre Tactical Training

John Chapman

Probably the most difficult decision when choosing a defensive training regimen is the decision to train at all. Making the leap from head in the sand civilian to condition-yellow armed citizen can be a painful evolutionary process. Luckily, a better selection of defensive training options has never been available. Until now. Today, there are scores of great schools and respected instructors available to us at highly reasonable fees.

Realizing you have not mastered the fundamental skills necessary to effectively defend yourself, your family or your teammates with firearms can be an ego buster. In order to get the most out of your training dollar, an unvarnished assessment of your skills and mindset are necessary. Before choosing a school, instructor or course, take a hard look at both your current skill set and the skill set you will reasonably and realistically need in the fight you are most likely to face. Write these down. Then being your research of schools or instructors who (at first glance) seem to focus on what you have identified as your needs.

Talk with instructors at the schools that seem to best fit what you think you need to learn. A reputable school will be happy to offer references. Would you hire a house painter without speaking to some of his past clients? Try to look past the explosions and cool-guy gear and find out if attendees are learning real-life skills and are able to practice them on their own after graduation. A high-speed course may be cool, but those lessons will dissipate quickly without follow-through on your part.

Once you have picked your school, attend with an open mind. Focus on what the instructor is trying to teach you, and keep your past practice or favorite techniques to yourself. You are paying a professional for instruction, so let him instruct. Take notes and take the handouts home. The act of taking notes will help you internalize the lessons and the handouts can serve as guides for dry-fire and live range practice sessions.

Finally, try to have fun while training. The more you enjoy it, the more often you will do it. Remember, amateurs practice until they get it right; professionals train until they can't get it wrong. Be professional, no matter what your profession may be.

John Chapman
LMS Training

Wes Doss

The post-911 world has yielded a tremendous number of private trainers and training organizations, giving the would-be student a massive menu of options from which to choose. Unfortunately, with this influx of training have come a number of options in trainers who are not really qualified to conduct training in their purported areas of expertise. It's important to remember that firearms training and tactics training, while crossing paths, are not necessarily the same thing. Teaching the mechanics of firearms training is one thing, but being able to speak intelligently about the dynamics of conflict and how best to manage situations requires a tremendous level of experience, a level frequently not held by the average trainer. This is not to suggest that everyone in uniform is an instructor, but rather not every trainer is a trainer in all disciplines. A student needs to know what kind of training they will be receiving and what, if any benefit, will be gleaned from that training.

Do your homework and check out the background of the instructors with which you intend to invest your time, energy and money. Validate the trainer, his/her actual background and find out who is their typical student. This sounds obvious, but trust me, it is seldom done and it can have a detrimental impact on you, your loved ones or your organization when it goes unchecked. Be guarded when you hear phrases like “The exclusive trainer to Naval Special Warfare” or “Sole Trainer to Major Metropolitan SWAT team.” Few of us in the training industry are masters of anything; most of us are just advanced students and when we have specialized clients. Rarely does a reputable instructor use mention of clients as a marketing tool.

Consider what training an instructor offers. If you’re looking for quality self-defense training for personal protection you probably won’t find it in a former Special Forces soldier, like-wise, if you’re looking for high-risk entry and breaching, you likely won’t find it through a local CCW instructor. Do your homework, find the best for your circumstances and get the most out of what’s offered.

Wes Doss
Khyber Interactive Associates

Craig Douglas

A Training Ethos

The mental framework an individual uses when approaching training can have a huge impact on the end result. Keeping a simple objective filter in position can mean the difference between continual advancement and inevitable stagnation. Apply a bifurcated ethos when evaluating a program and progress:

Be honest.

And do the work.

Sounds simple doesn't it?

Being honest to the problem is more difficult that it sounds. Everyone engages in some level of self-deception about who they are. A good shooter who is grossly obese is probably going to be more inclined to focus on his marksmanship than to utilize that same time on the treadmill. Why? We tend to do the things we're good at. A good self-image is critical to self esteem and when it really comes down to brass tacks, most people train because they *want* to, not because they *have* to. Neither is training always the means toward holistic, fluid and combative proficiency. Sometimes it's ego bolstering. In the case of the overweight shooter, he may perceive that his accuracy and speed can be incrementally shaved down from an already solid base. But he refuses to acknowledge that the stress of the fight may send him into cardiac arrest.

Doing the work means just that. Human beings are generally creatures who seek the path of least resistance. They would much rather hear that a shortcut will yield the same results as tedious discipline. This mindset encourages combative systems that promise one can dominate an adversary by simply applying a technique from the sacred scrolls. It's much less *work* to surf Internet forums for advice on a set of sights than it is to go dry-fire for 30 minutes on a Sunday, accomplishing more with less.

Develop your own ethos (or adopt the one here) to drive your approach to training, the selection process and ultimate performance with a consistent, objective mental framework.

Lt. Craig S. Douglas (a.k.a. SouthNarc)
Shivworks

John S. Farnam

At the top of my advice regarding shooting/tactics instruction is: Don't put it off! Shooting and tactics are like so many other critical life skills, especially as we're plummeting headlong into an era of exciting world history. Knowledge is the thin membrane that separates the quick from the dead!

When you walk into class, leave your ego outside. Come to class to learn. Neither your instructor nor your fellow students are interested in how wonderful you are. None of them think it should be you who is teaching the class. And while not everyone in the class will start at the same skill level, all students need to have a healthy, discerning and enthusiastic attitude and be open to learning.

Don't come with the expectation of being entertained. Don't expect to have fun. Don't plan to relax. Competent instruction is not about making you look good. It is grueling, hard work. Looking good is of interest only to the shallow and self-centered. Competent instruction is always a tempestuous mixture of success and failure. Real learning takes place when you fail. Little is ever learned from success, but enough success needs to be included in the mix to keep students motivated and moving forward. When success is too easily attained, you are simply striving toward the insignificant!

Your instructor should always lead the way, live-demonstrating every drill. You need to see it done and know it can be done, before starting to learn how to do it yourself. Instructors who hesitate to boldly step forward and lead/show/demonstrate the way are always suspect.

Understand that some of the instruction will be dry. We try to make it as interesting and exciting as we can, but, in order for you to be a well-rounded and competent operator, you need to be intimately acquainted with a broad scope of subjects and skills. Some are more interesting than others—but all are important.

Finally, expose yourself to as many good instructors as you can. None of us are perfect. None of us own the only true way. We are students too!

John S. Farnam
Defense Training International

Tom Givens

Years ago, I attended a street survival course in which the instructor stated that all training should meet the Three R Test. To be valuable, training should be Relevant, Realistic and Recent. It's a practice that has a lot of merit.

Relevant. With the cost of both travel and ammunition rising constantly, the issue of selecting relevant training becomes critical. Sure, it's fun to do a military carbine course and fire 1500-2000 rounds through your AR over the weekend, and get your flight suit and chest rig dirty. How likely are you to have those items handy when assaulted on the parking lot of the Stop 'n Rob? If training funds/time are limited, as they are for most people, how about concentrating on the skills you might actually have reason to use? My suggestion: enroll in thorough and ongoing training with an everyday carry concealed handgun, plus at least one weekend course on the defensive shotgun. The handgun can be your constant companion, and for home or business defense, the shotgun is a valuable addition. If you want to take a contractor's carbine course as a fun vacation, recognize it for that, and don't count it against your training budget.

Realistic. Again, look at your actual likely defensive requirements. Find a trainer who teaches actual concealed carry methods, not just range drills with open carry ceremonial holsters. Remind yourself not to train with a 5" 1911 worn openly and then leave the range with a j-frame in your pocket. Train with and carry gear you can actually fight with. Fundamentals are always the key to performance, so spend your time wisely, working on the skills actually involved in defensive shootings.

Recent. Skills involved in fighting, whether empty-handed, with a blade or with a gun, are highly perishable. You need frequent refresher training under a qualified instructor. Then you need to practice! Remember the distinction between training and practice. Training is acquiring new skills. Practice is ingraining those skills into your response system so that they can be recalled and executed under duress. Last year in the United States, almost 14 million people were the victims of serious, felonies and violent crime. In my city, you have about a 1 in 100 chance of being the victim of an aggravated assault each year. So, get off your butt and train now. One day you will be glad you did.

Tom Givens
Rangemaster

Paul Haberstroh

"Practice does not make perfect. Perfect practice makes perfect". A great defensive shooting program is more like Special Ed. than Special Forces, emphasizing the fundamentals that are the foundation of successful learning and training.

Regardless of your experience or skill level, there is always room to evolve your skills and become a more efficient shooter. The best PGA Tour players consistently take lessons to hone their skills. Shooting like any other sport has benefited from advances in research, technology and science. A great program embraces and integrates these discoveries.

A great shooting teacher is just that. Someone who will help you understand and execute the skills and techniques to become efficient and consistent. A great instructor will recognize and capitalize on learning opportunities so that you can recognize them also when you practice. Skill is not skill if it is not consistent and it is up to you to become competent.

Your training must be consistent and realistic and your training must be applicable to real world situations in a real world environment. It is not likely you will be attacked at the shooting range from 25 yards away.

There is some dogma in the shooting instruction world and some inflexible old school mindsets. While there is always something to be learned from these teachers, make sure the training is applicable to your needs.

Paul Haberstroh
Colorado Firearms Academy

Denny Hansen

Almost every tactical firearms course I have attended (and I have attended hundreds) has addressed how to clear malfunctions, be it handgun or rifle/carbine. A few classes, however, have ever addressed the *cause* of malfunctions. The simple fact of the matter is that when firearms are fired, the parts inside them are subjected to wear. If fired often enough, those parts—springs, extractors, magazines—will wear to the point that the shooter begins to experience malfunctions.

To track how many rounds I have fired, I keep a weapon log—sometimes called a gun book—on all my firearms. This log has a space for round count, type of training, detail on the magazines used (You do number your mags and keep track of those causing problems, right?), accessories added (rails, lights or lasers) and parts replaced.

While not an exact science, there are some general guidelines that indicate when parts are being worn to the point of inducing malfunctions--frequency and in some case the rate (i.e., full-auto) that a firearm is fired. A few basic parts to monitor are:

Extraction issues. Experienced on a fairly regular

basis, they are most often presented by a Type One (stovepipe) and sometimes by a Type Three (double feed). In addition to the extractor itself (check yours to make sure it still has a sharp edge), these common malfunctions can be caused by a recoil spring that has lost some of its power. Check with your manufacturer and find out at what point the recoil spring should be replaced. Shooting mostly 1911-type pistols, I replace the recoil springs in my pistols between 3,000-4,000 rounds, and the extractor at around 6,000 rounds. (Note: It's a good idea to also replace the firing pin spring when replacing the recoil spring to ensure the stronger inertia from the new spring will not overpower the firing pin spring.) Replacing the springs as recommended will not only help reduce malfunctions, they will prolong the frame life of the pistol.

Maintenance. Maintaining a weapon log for AR-15-type rifles and carbines is of paramount importance. Bolts can need replacement after 6,000 rounds and *should* be replaced after 10,000. The extractor, spring and insert should be replaced at 5,000 rounds, and the bolt rings between 1,500 and 3,000.

Record keeping. It's aggravating to encounter an endless string of malfunctions during a training course due to a bad part. On the two-way range, it literally means the difference between life and death. The best way to track the parts that need replacing is by starting and continually updating a weapon log.

Stay low and watch your back.

Denny Hansen
Editor, *S.W.A.T. Magazine*

Gila Hayes

When looking for defense skills training, ask for recommendations at the range, the gun store, at competitive venues and from acquaintances that are martial artists or defensive shooters. Call the schools recommended and ask enough questions to be sure you start at the level appropriate to your skills. Ask if the school has any materials–books, articles, DVDs–that will help you prepare for class, or if they can recommend such resources.

When you go to a class, take your "beginner's mind." Leave your earlier experiences at home, and prepare to explore new or modified techniques. To get the most out of your training dollar, wait until after class is over to discard techniques you believe don't work. Sort, keep and discard methods only after you have been exposed to the entire body of class material.

Bring a "can do" attitude to class. Do not utter the phrase, "I can't, because...." A good, professional instructor will do their utmost to help a student who genuinely strives to perform the skills taught in class. But even the best teacher eventually becomes discouraged by long-winded explanations that start with "I can't...."

Ask questions. During class, keep questions focused on the topic under discussion, but do not be afraid on breaks to ask the instructor about issues that have gone unmentioned. Keep in mind that classes are usually focused on specific topics or portions of the defensive spectrum. While most instructors are happy to field off-topic questions during breaks or after class, it may be best to also ask, "Where can I find this information?" This approach may be most true when discussing legal issues involving police and the courts, especially when inquiring about laws outside the instructor's home area. Remember, your instructor is more than likely a skilled shooter or martial artist–not an attorney.

After class, continue your study of the topics learned, whether that means reading books and articles, or reviewing materials on DVDs. Go to the range, or find a partner with which to practice the defense skills you learned. Keep those skills sharp. Class time is devoted to teaching you the techniques. It is your responsibility to keep those new techniques well practiced.

Gila Hayes
The Firearms Academy of Seattle, Inc.

Marty Hayes

When considering who to train with and where to train, your first concern should be how your training will look in court.If you need to defend your actions in ether criminal or civil court, discovery will likely introduce the preparations you have made to use deadly force.Depending on the quality of training you have received, it may either help or hurt.For example, if you have extensively trained at the latest high-speed, low-drag schools where the course title conjures up images of wild Rambo types, that *could* come back to haunt you. On the other hand, class titles using descriptive terms like "legal, ethical, responsible" should help. Your training should be balanced between studying the legal and moral aspects of use of deadly force, along with skill development.Consider how a course listing will play to a jury in Peoria.

Additionally, if asked to testify in court on your behalf, will your trainer or trainershelp or hurt you?If charged with a crime or sued for use of deadly force in an incident, you have to defend yourself in court by proffering the "defense of self-defense." When you invoke the "defense of self-defense," you also admit to the killing, but claim it was justified.When you do this, you additionally shift the burden of proof to your claim of self-defense, which means you need to call witnesses in court to give evidence that your act of killing was justified.One or more witnesses called may be your trainers. They can legitimately testify as to what they taught you in a particular training course.Will the background of your trainer stand up in court?What is his experience in the legal arena?Will scrutiny of his or her background pass muster?

Jeff Cooper called the legal aftermath of a self-defense shooting Problem Two, and while it is indeed the second priority in resolving a deadly force encounter, it is still a priority.Surviving a deadly attack against you or your loved ones is like fighting a house fire.The first priority is to get everyone out alive.Once that's accomplished, then you turn your attention to saving your pets and your home. If you cannot save the residence, do you have insurance to replace it? The armed defender needs to ensure against a legal attack. That means studying the legal issues and making sure thatif your actions are questioned in court, you will be able to justify those actions. Study and train with the best in the business to handle Problem One, but don't forget Problem Two.

Marty Hayes

The Armed Citizens' Legal Defense Network, LLC.

Michael Janich

An Open Mind, a Grain of Salt, and a Clear Understanding of Your Own Goals

Evaluating instructors in the tactical/personal defense industry can be an interesting challenge. In addition to trying to determine their actual proficiency at the skills they proclaim to teach, you also need to evaluate their skills as a teacher and the relevance of their approach to the topic to your needs. With these criteria in mind, here's a quick guide to finding an instructor that meets your needs:

First, confirm that the instructor can actually perform the skills that you want to develop—and he purports to teach—competently. As obvious as this may sound, the training community (and particularly the martial arts and self-defense world) is full of overweight, out-of-shape masters whose deadliest weapons are flapping gums and their own gravitational pull. The bottom line: They must be able to do what you want to learn how to do.

Second, and the most often overlooked criterion, is skill at teaching. We've all heard the cliché "Those who can, do; those who can't, teach." That's amusing. But what if the thing you want someone to do *is* to teach and he can't? The answer: You don't learn.

Teaching is a skill, an art, and to some, a gift. Think of the best and worst teachers you had in school and you'll immediately understand what I'm talking about. So when you're considering a tactical instructor, don't just look at his skills as an operator, look at his ability to explain those skills in a clear, logical manner. Then consider his ability to evaluate your skills, provide clear corrective feedback, and enable you to develop your proficiency in a progressive manner. That's a teacher.

Finally, make sure that what the instructor teaches is relevant to your needs and goals. If you're a civilian concerned with responsible personal defense and everything the instructor teaches is presented in the context of team tactics for a SWAT team, it's not relevant to your needs, as cool as the course might be. And, if you ingrain it too deeply, it may cause you to develop tactical habits that only work when you're fully kitted out and have a stack of guys with you, rather than when you're carrying concealed and all alone.

The best instructors are the ones that enable YOU to effectively learn the skills that YOU need most to stay safe. If you keep that in mind, you'll get the most out of your teachers and your training.

Michael Janich
Martial Blade Concepts

Tiger McKee

Train And Practice

To properly fight with firearms requires training - an introduction to effective techniques and theory – and practice - to learn and improve those skills. The real learning process begins when your training class is over; it takes three to five thousand repetitions of an action for it to become ingrained into your subconscious. The best way to develop and hone these fighting skills is dry-practice.

In most peoples' minds this practice takes place on the range, but few of us have the time or money for that much live-fire practice. Dry-fire practice - working repetitions with you weapon - is key. What most people don't realize is that their daily lives contain countless opportunities to practice without even using a weapon. During a commercial break, on your trip to the fridge, pretend you've got your firearm, moving tactically, working corners and using cover. Eventually your family will get used to this, and you'll be gaining valuable practice. At the restaurant, look around, imagining your response if something goes bad. Take five minutes each day, sit back, eyes closed and vividly imagine confronting a threat, creating distance and using cover. This practice cultivates a readiness that you can't get from shooting live ammo on the range.

To fight effectively the mind and body must be seamless. Action immediately follows thought. The more you think about a skill - repetition for the brain – and the more you practice the physical actions, the better you perform. Hagakure, The Book of the Samurai, advises, "Throughout your life advance daily, becoming more skillful than yesterday, more skillful than today. This is never-ending." By being motivated and creative, dry-practice can be part of your daily life. Everything you do contains a tactical learning experience.

Tiger McKee
Shootrite Firearms Academy

Gary Meares

Mind on Gear

The common link between all warriors is the equipment we choose to go into battle with. As important as the guy next to you, so is your gear. So what's your choice? If you have ever wandered the numbered isles of the Shot Show or been down to the local tactical supply shop, the amount of equipment is staggering. How does the mindful warrior determine the best kit for the task? And bear in mind not performing that task, can and will result in very bad things happening. The job alone is daunting, let alone the chance of a strap, snap, Velcro, molle, sling, weaver mount or what ever is holding the gear coming loose. Because it will.

To me, the best gear is simple gear and if it worked on the last 100 ops, it will work again. I understand the latest, greatest, got to have product is out there, but is it proven and time tested? I remember as a young operator standing in briefing for a warrant. When we were done with the brief back, our team leader had us line up and do a series of running in place, push-ups and side straddle hops. Gear was falling off and making noise all down the line. It was clear what needed to be done, and we did it. If it is not mission specific, leave it behind and ensure the gear is secure.

PACFW. That is Protection (*body armor, weapons)*, Ammo, Comm, Food and Water. These are the essentials for any Op. I have seen the 1 hour search warrant turn into a protracted 12 hour barricade. That is a bad spot to be in hungry and thirsty. There are a ton of energy food/water products on the market. I would rather have a mushy Power bar in July than nothing.

If you need one, make sure your tac -vest is up to grade. It should provide plenty of room for magazines. I prefer my secondary weapon on my chest, not my leg and communications gear should go in the front, not the back. Training days should be in "full gear" you have to know the kit is reliable and functional. New guys, look to the senior guys to see what they are wearing and how they wear it. All weapons carried have to be flashlight capable with spare batteries, always. Do you carry a personal first aid kit? Does everyone on the team know where you carry it? Gear up the same way, every time. Don't get caught up in the latest gear craze. If it is truly a piece of gear you need, you'll know it. Just spend some time thinking about what you carry and why you carry it.

Remain Motivated,

Lt Gary Meares (ret)
DGG Taser & Tactical Supply

John Meyer

It was the great eighteenth century Russian Field Marshal Aleksandr Vasilevich Suvorov (1729-1800), who first said, "Train hard, fight easy." I'm a believer in Suvorov's philosophy. It's the foundation of the way I train—and the way I train others to train. After all, our number-one mission as trainers is to keep the officers we train alive, and the harder you work during training, the less you'll bleed on the streets.As an Instructor, I tell all my students, I am not here to test what you already know. I believe that an Instructor's job is to teach skills to make good decisions. The way we learn to make good decisions is through experience. Experience is gained through doing, Do not be afraid to make bad decisions in training, you will learn from them. Try a new or unfamiliar technique, training is the time to try new things. However, trying a technique 1-3 times and giving up on it is not giving it a fair evaluation.

Remember the difference between training and education, training is the act of doing, education is providing knowledge. Easer way to understand the difference is; would you rather have your teen age children go to Sex education or Sex training?

When you select a training event make sure it's training, not just education, and be sure you use your training time wisely.

Here is an example of two boxers and two training regimes. They are both on the same diet and get the same amount of rest:

Boxer 1, two hours of each of the exercises below.

1. Running
2. Jumping Rope
3. Heavy Bag
4. Speed Bag
5. Weight Training
6. Shadow Training

Boxer 2, one hour of each exercise, (above). Who will be in better shape in one month? Boxer #2 will spend the hour between each exercise sparring with a different boxer every day.

Now who will be the better boxer?

I believe in dynamic, realistic training. This method oftraining should teach students not just how to handle weapons, but how to handle situations. That's the bottom line: realistic, dynamic training gives students the tools they need in order to survive and prevail in the real world. Realistic, dynamic training forces students to think for themselves, and to push further and harder than they ever have before.

Good Luck in your training.

Train to Win.

John T. Meyer, Jr.

Team One Network

Peter Moll

Nineteen years ago, I started my training in Escrima. It took me some time to realize something important: as I tried to master techniques for all the possible different situations that could come up in a fight. I realized that it was impossible to master a technique for all possibilities with every weapon. My focus shifted to the concepts behind the techniques. Once I understood and mastered the concepts of defensive and offensive techniques, I found that I was able to train much more efficiently. I also found that I needed fewer Techniques. A few solid concepts can be the basis for effective and efficient responses to countless specific situations. Search for your underlying concepts and principles to guide your training and selection of techniques, then set about mastering the techniques

Peter Moll
I.C.E. Staff Instructor, Germany

Ken Murray

A lot of people seem to think that Reality Based Training (RBT) requires a lot of staff, specialized facilities and equipment, and that it is complex, costly and dangerous. Depending on the method of RBT, this indeed may be true, however I tell my students in RTB that the "How To" class for scenarios is actually the *second* class. The first class consists of a collection of drills–the steps if you will–to the ultimate dance. Much like ballroom dancing, the martial arts fight is the culmination of learning and mastering a collection of smaller skills. You cannot dance if you don't know the steps. You cannot fight if you haven't learned the basics. Talk to any master of anything, and they will tell you that they are experts at the basics. Effective performance is simply the smooth application of the basics. Analyze any horrific incident perpetrated by society's evil-doers and you can make the judgment that if responders failed, they failed at the basics. When responders succeeded, it was through an application of basic techniques.

RBT encompasses the mastery of the basics through training and repetition, then performing a crisis rehearsal of a critical incident in a contextual setting using role playing and realistic training versions of actual equipment. Those who do well in real-life RBT have done the work in advance in scenarios. They hone their skills in the fires of mock battle. Those who have not done the work in advance will perform poorly in real-life, failing at basic functions such as improper movement or use of cover, inappropriate choice and application of force options or a complete meltdown under the stress of conflict.

Take a success-based building block approach to your training—small increments of success layered on previous successes. Work towards small and successful changes over a longer period of time rather than attempting to effect large changes in a short period of time.

Mariners have a saying: An inch on the nose equals a mile on the horizon. It's a mathematical fact. If you change your course by one inch while traveling in any direction, by the time you reach the horizon, you will end up at a point one mile from where you would have landed had you not veered off course by an inch at the nose.

Ken Murray
Armiger Police Training Institute

Kent O'Donnell

When considering which tactical course to attend, read the course description and also speak to the instructor or course coordinator. I have found that tactical courses often reflect the students in attendance; a class with a group of students experienced in a particular tactical skill can move faster than a group without that shared expertise. By speaking with the instructor or coordinator, you can proactively learn if the class you're considering is right for you.

Choose a facility or instructor that is "time tested." Just because they hang a sign out that says they are an instructor does not mean they have the experience to deliver the promised training. You do not want to have your instructor here today and gone tomorrow. I also encourage you to keep handouts and reference material—particularly materials that pertain to use of force issues. As reference guides, these handouts can be beneficial, and also a good way to vet whether the training is correct.

Kent O'Donnell
Blacksheep Training

Tim O'Rourke

What are you, as a student, looking for? Put your Goggle skills to work and you'll find dozens of choices for whatever kind of training you're looking for on the web. From public speaking to defensive shooting, it's available at www.something-or-another.com.

Then narrow your subject list down to a handful of instructors. Yes, instructors. Harvard may be the name that gets you an ideal job, but it is knowledge gained from your instructors' experience and skill that matters in shooting. Don't make the mistake of choosing your training sources based solely on a school name. Contrary to conventional wisdom, institutions do not train students; instructors train students.

What are your goals? Gaining new skills? Polishing old skills? Career development? In-service training? Continuing education units? Recertification? Requalification?

Whatever your goal is, commit yourself 100 percent to getting everything out of training that you can. Every 100 percent student leaves training with new skills or knowledge and understands these are often perishable—use them or loose them. A lesser student will often leave with the best of intentions, and within a month or so, will rationalize all kinds of reasons that they cannot stay current on a skill.

A 100 percent student knows that superior firearms skills alone will not win a fight, just as the fastest car will not win Daytona. Your 100 percent instructor will share this secret with you if you're listening. It takes more than just skill sets to win. M-E-S-S is the acronym for Mental, Emotional and Skill Sets. Keep your MESS in alignment. This Training Log should prompt you to consider, "What did I do this week to keep my MESS together?"

Tim O'Rourke
S2 Institute

Troy Price

Whether preparing to embark on a long training regimen, or taking your first class, the best advice I can give to a student is "use quality equipment that you're willing to bet your life on".

Your training goals should be to learn new skills and to improve upon skills you already possess. It is easy to get distracted from these goals if you are fighting your gear.

Many students embarking upon training for the first time do not want to purchase high dollar equipment; and that is understandable. Often the student is not sure if the endeavor they are embarking on warrants or requires output of hard-earned cash.

I have seen all too often students coming to class with low-end firearms, cheap nylon holsters, no magazine pouches. As often as not, these students spend much of the class fighting weapons and holster malfunctions or watching equipment falling apart. When this happens the students aren't able to apply the necessary amount of focus on the skills being taught for their time trying to figure out how to overcome the shortfalls of the equipment.

You can often place equipment options into one of three categories: Low-cost, average cost and high end. All of this equipment must be looked at objectively. Most manufacturers of quality equipment will fall into the "average cost" and "high end" categories. The manufacturers are giving choices to people that want their gear to stand up to long-term hard use.

The "low cost" equipment manufacturers are often attempting to break into a market and make a quick buck. They do this by marketing to the individual that may only use the equipment once or twice, recreationally. The type who won't experience what will happen during hard use. The problems start when that gear is brought to a quality course by an eager student and fails.

If your firearm cannot make it through a 2-day class without a malfunction, then you shouldn't be relying on it to save your life. Your equipment must function every time, all the time, without fail. If it doesn't you shouldn't be using it. Even malfunctions in training can hurt you. The firearm that doesn't function properly, the holster that doesn't cover the trigger guard, or the glasses that aren't to standard can present safety hazards that can cause permanent and irreversible damage even in training. Choose gear carefully and wisely. Spending a few extra dollars may save your hours of frustration and help you make the most of your valuable, and limited, training time.

Troy Price
LMS Training

Tony Scotti

When selecting a training program, do your homework. Get information about the program or programs of interest—the best information comes from a prior attendee. Get reassurance that the referring party had the same motivation for training as you do. Most everyone will say they had a great time, so specifically ask what they learned. Did it meet or exceed their expectations. If not, why? If not, it could be that the training was okay but not what the student wanted. When you are doing your research examine the curriculum carefully, is it what you want.

Be suspect of the brochure or website that promotes a facility and/or equipment and mentions little about the instructors. Yes, you need to have good equipment and a good facility, but you can have both of those and if the instructor can't teach, you won't learn anything. The instructor's bio should cover his teaching qualifications. Contrary to popular belief, not everyone can teach. Teaching requires experience, knowledge and the most important quality: the ability to transfer that knowledge to others. It's not easy.

Prior to commencing exercises, an apt instructor

will explain the goals and objectives of the exercises. Ask yourself, “Why am I doing this and what is the relevance of this to my world?” You don’t want to complete a training program with a false sense of what you can and cannot do. Some forms of tactical training can measure skills relatively easily; tactical driving is not one of them. But whether it’s easy or not is a mute point as every tactical training program has to objectively measure your skill level—driving is no different. Tactical driving requires precision, tenths of seconds and 2 MPH. A few inches variation on your grip on the steering wheel can mean the difference between success and failure. Those are things that cannot be measured with the naked eye. While attending a tactical driving program, your progress and skill level needs to be measured with on-board computers and/or with a radar gun, stop watch and a calibrated scenario.

Don’t mistake adrenalin for education. Most training programs produce adrenalin at some level.

Tony Scotti
Tony Scotti Associates

Clint Smith

The ability to use firearms effectively for most people is a skill acquired more by repetition than by being an act of nature. These skills once acquired are constantly under duress and can diminish by the lack of use or just by the simple fact that if we live long enough, we grow older and muscles wane and eyes will fail.

To acquire initial and advanced skills requires an open mind and a realization that there is very little magic at play and the key component to gaining firearms and tactical skills is hard work.

There is no room to argue that the most effective way to use firearms is to properly align the sights and place and hold those sights on target while manipulating the trigger to have the weapon fire. The ability or potential to use this most effective of firing techniques can and probably will be influenced by environment, visual acuity and the overall fog of conflict. Yet in reality after marksmanship expertise and probably even before it the knowledge and use of individual personal awareness and personal tactics know-how, will determine the outcome of the action as much as weapons skills.

My preference for students would be that they

train and work to be smart over being strong. As we grow old we will not be as strong… but we can always be smart.

Logic is the cornerstone of what I try to teach. All students and teachers alike need to ask themselves if what they are learning, teaching and practicing is logical and true to the world they live in to the best of their knowledge.

Clint Smith
Thunder Ranch Inc.

Randy Smith

Fighting vs. Shooting

Target shooting is fun...self-defense shooting is deadly serious. If you are serious about defensive training, be sure to take courses that are fighting oriented. Other than the gun and some handling skills, target shooting and defensive shooting have very little in common. There is a misconception among much of the public that a basic pistol or target shooting course will prepare you to use a gun for self-defense. Nothing could be further from the truth.

Target and competition schools have great value, but most likely will not impart the mind set, skill set, or the knowledge you need to win a lethal force encounter. In fact, the learned skill that gets you a better time/score in a match, may very well get you killed on the street. You need to learn to stop the lethal threat as effectively and efficiently as possible, not how to get a better score.

Target and competition shooting classes are a lot of fun. Serious self-defense training is a lot of work. Do some soul searching to determine your true interests and pursue training that will enhance your personal skills.

And remember, wearing 5.11 pants doesn't make you tactical…being tactical makes you tactical.

Randy Smith
Professional Firearms Training

Robert Smith, M.D.

"An operator should train, eat and sleep all with about the same level of enthusiasm."

-Jeff Martone

When training becomes integrated into lifestyle, *then* it is true training.

Training must be applicable to what the operator is doing. It must reflect an approach that is sourced from someone who is humble enough to realize that they do not know everything, but studious enough to have analyzed problems from multiple perspectives with the ability to communicate lessons learned both succinctly and effectively.

True training comes from an individual that is able to coach a student into efficient utilization of energy, movement *and* thought. This coaching capability is the result of integrating listening, seeing and knowing a student's potential performance capability.

How an operator absorbs new information is unique to that person, and is a result of his ability to apply that information. Fundamentally, the usefulness of training is a function of the operator's educational and environmental adaptability, and the instructor's ability to effect two-way communication.

With all of this said however, the most realistic obstacles that educators and trainers have is the acquisition of new knowledge and communicating that knowledge to those who would excel at their combative art. Likewise, operators have the regrettable tendency to not train daily in their combative disciplines. The combination of these factors is the challenge to be met by those that would dedicate their lives to teaching and learning combative skills.

Training must become a lifestyle that is perpetuated by educational curiosity, technical discipline, and professional commitment to prepare for the fight.

Robert Smith, M.D.
Direct Action Medical Network

Dave Spaulding

As a student of armed combat for my entire adult life, I experienced my first disappointment in my training regarding the combative use of the revolver at basic police academy. New to the skill, I began to interview everyone I could find who had been in a gunfight. My first interview was with an aging veteran who sat with a shaking hand and a tear in his eye as he told me what it was like to fight bayonet to bayonet in a muddy trench. Since that time, I've spoken with hundreds of such people and the one thing that I have learned is that the simple techniques are best.

I have devised a short test that I share with students to use as they begin their journey toward defensive proficiency. Ask yourself:

- Is the technique or tactic you are learning *Simple* to perform? If it's not *Simple* on the range or in the gym, do you think it will become easier in a fight?
- Does the technique make *Sense* to you? You may bring to the table a wealth of experience, possibly including extensive prior training, but if the technique doesn't make

sense vis-à-vis your experience, talk with the instructor and see if this can be corrected.

Finally, is the technique *Steet* proven? If not, do you want to be the guinea pig?

It has been my experience that this "Three S Test" separates the relevant from the "Tacti-Flash," the worthwhile from the crap. I hope this helps and good luck. Stay safe, alert and Check 360 often!

Dave Spaulding
Author, *Handgun Combatives*

Andy Stanford

Selecting an instructor or school today is both easier and more difficult than it was just a few short decades ago when I began my own quest for specialized knowledge and skill. It's easier because there are significantly more qualified individuals plying their trade now than in the recent past. It's more difficult because the proliferation of credible trainers can make choosing among them a daunting proposition. As a graduate of dozens of world-class courses, I offer the following guidelines:

Do your homework. A little research can go a long way in choosing the right trainer(s) for your needs. The internet makes it easier than ever to obtain recommendations from previous students and colleagues. One caveat: always consider the source of any endorsement. Someone who has trained primarily or exclusively with a single instructor or doctrine may lack perspective and be somewhat less than objective.

Study the big picture. Preparing for self-defense and/or tactical operations will require that you address four primary topics: Mindset, Tactics, Skill, and Equipment. The first three comprise the human factors that you will develop during training and practice and the key is to work on all of them. Many people confuse technical shooting skill with the ability to win a fight.

Avail yourself of all available resources. Concurrent with the explosion of instructors, the amount of written and video material on the topics at hand has increased greatly. Many top trainers have written books and produced DVDs on their doctrine and techniques, and these can be a cost-effective way to broaden your perspective and evaluate candidates for your patronage.

Keep an open mind. In truth, most instructors have something to offer, but none have all the answers. I must confess to being quite dogmatic in my early days, with a somewhat blind allegiance to the dogma of my Gun Guru of choice. Once I took off the blinders, my own expertise increased exponentially, as did the level of training I offer.

Continue to learn, train, and practice. No matter what the length, one course will not ingrain the skills in question. You must put in the effort required to make your techniques and tactics reflexive, otherwise they will not be available under the stress of a life-threatening situation. Additionally, commit to taking professional instruction on a regular basis. If you teach for a living, this is particularly important. My personal motto is "Sometimes a teacher; always a student."

As you study and train, keep your overall objective in mind and stock your tactical toolbox accordingly.

Armed professionals are paid to deal with danger, but the private citizen has the luxury of preempting it whenever possible. Always remember that regardless of your goal, your number one option for personal security is a commitment to avoidance, deterrence and de-escalation.

Andy Stanford
Options for Personal Safety

Colin Tinnin

There is a simple theme among vast amount of students that is often heard in regards to finding good training. “Just go to a course because you will take at least one new tool home for your tool bag.” This is great advice for the guy that you don’t like and want to see spend thousands of dollars and watch his head spin every time he comes home.

The best advice that I have heard thus far is find an instructor that teaches the most realistic and relevant training for your own personal needs It is often seen and easily confusing for students but fast doesn’t always mean efficient. Take a good hard look at the material being taught and keep an open mind when doing your research; it could change your life.

The other important thing to look for in an instructor is his or hers ability to teach and articulate concepts. You want to avoid the instructor that can’t explain why they’re having you do something or consistently telling you to do something because it’s fast. There are new and innovative training techniques out there being taught by great instructors and it is up to the student to seek them out. You Should take the training and determine for yourself if you agree with the concepts.

Training should be safe and fun not intimidating and nerve-racking. Keep an open mind and train and practice hard. Do your best to become great at all self-defense, not just things that go bang.

Colin Tinnin
360 Tactical Training and Self Defense

Mark Warren & Vaughn Baker

One of the main factors related to training has to be the ability to identify what your career goals are. If you know where you want to go you will know how to get there.

We believe in a building block approach to training and it makes sense for most everyone. Many times you see enthusiastic students that are new to this career field and too many times their money is somewhat wasted because they are taking an advanced course before they are ready.

Evaluate your skills, understand your strengths and focus on improving your weaknesses. We too often spend our valuable training time training to do what we are already good at instead of focusing our energy on our deficiencies. Our strengths will carry us; our weaknesses will get us hurt.

Study the finite details of the fight or the engagement. We have been fortunate to evaluate and study thousands of hours of video from force on force training. This insight has proven that the critical process of prevailing in the fight is not at the point of pulling the trigger but instead it is the important decisions and positioning prior to pulling the trigger. Just like a good ground fighter, he does not try a submission hold until he is in the proper position to apply the appropriate technique. Many accept this principle as it relates to ground fighting but are skeptical when we tell you it does not change because you are fighting with a different weapons platform.

Lastly, enter all training with an open mind, apply your self and give everything an honest try. Our biggest mistake is we want to believe that once we leave the training course we are fully competent and completely trained. Keep in mind that we have several stages to go through, the first is unconscious incompetence. We don't know what we don't know. Once we are made aware we become conscious incompetent, meaning we at least know we are lacking in our ability. Then through proper training we can reach conscious competence, you are capable of applying the technique and/or principle but it can usually only be done consciously. This is generally the level you are at when you leave a training course. You have invested time and money in your training don't allow it to go to waste because when you leave the course you have decided your are good enough and do not continue to practice what you have learned. If you will continue to practice and train you will reach the final level we all should strive for; unconscious competence, everything done and applied without thought.

Good luck with your training and remember can you ever be good enough in a fight? You know what your skills are but we never know the actual ability of our adversary.

Mark Warren & Vaugh Baker
Strategos International

Claude Werner

Before the course, prepare yourself for it as much as possible. If the instructor has written books or produced videos, read or watch them. Write down any questions so you can get them clarified during the class. Do what you can to get your baseline skill level as high as you can prior to the course.

Check your equipment's functionality before the course rather than planning to use the course as a weapons check. When you get to the class you want to focus on the course material, not getting your equipment running properly. If you have new equipment, break it in prior to the course. For a rifle class, zero your rifle and know its zero at various ranges ahead of time. For a pistol class, shoot an IPSC or IDPA match with your pistol to make sure it and your ammunition are reliable and that your holster suits you. If possible, have and bring a second weapon in case you primary becomes non-mission capable.

During the course, be open minded to the course material. Your objective in attending should be to learn new skills, not validate what you already know. Once you are done with the class, you can decide which parts of its theory and techniques you wish to retain or discard.

Take care of yourself physically during the training. Hydrate, eat, rest, etc as necessary. Don't allow yourself to become a casualty. You will learn much more if you keep yourself in good shape throughout the course.

After the course, practice what you have learned. The class only provides an overview of the techniques you learned; you MUST practice them for a while after the class to ingrain them at a subconscious level. At the end of the course, ask the instructor how to practice what you have learned. Establish a benchmark of your skill level at the end of the course and then try to raise the bar for that benchmark in the weeks and months after the course is over.

Claude Werner
Rogers Shooting School

James Yeager

I remember my very first training class. It was very exciting and a little scary. Who were the other pistoleros? Would they laugh at me? Would they be safe? I asked myself several times "Am I good enough to even take this course?"

I know now that many first time students think that same thing prior to signing up. I have also seen many people who think that professional training has nothing to offer them.

If your experience is similar to mine, your first class will have the highest amount of information you will ever take from one lesson. Why? Because shooting isn't too complex and after you get the fundamentals and technique there isn't a lot left, no matter how high Speed the course advertisement looks.

Nobody wants to take a "basic" level class. Everyone wants an "advanced" class because they are above anything else. I hate to be the one who breaks it to you but they are all pretty much the same. Sure advanced classes are different but not too much. Take basic classes. They contain a lot of very good information. I have taken many basic classes and I learned a lot from every single one of them. I have found that less than 10% of shooters have a firm grasp on shooting fundamentals and yet 90% think they shouldn't be demoted to anything less than an advanced class. All that said, I would like to pass along some information that might make your tuition at your next firearms training class go further.

The Golden Rule is to have an OPEN MIND. Go to every class with the opinion you know nothing. Push all of your previous training to the side and do the class EXACTLY like the Instructor tells you. Even if the Instructor tells you to do something that is alien or never worked for you in the past.

If you think you know more than the instructor I advise you to keep quiet. It is his class and if you want to teach you should start your own school. I did. What you shouldn't do is interrupt him; it is disruptive to the entire class. If you have a valid point to make wait for a break in the lecture, he will want to hear it. Please don't tutor other students. They didn't pay to hear your opinions.

No matter how good your favorite school may be you have to train at different places. If your school tells you to never do "this" go find a school that says to always do it. Go to as many different types of learning environments as possible.

Show up for class on time and be prepared to stay. I have been to schools that you "trained" 5 hours out of the 8 and yet others where you where begging for a break. Get plenty of sleep, don't get drunk the night before class, and , remember my

Golden Rule: *come to learn with an open mind* and you will get the most for your training dollar!

James Yeager
Tactical Response

Training Resources

360 Tactical Training & Self Defense
Colin TInnin
Houston, TX
www.memorialshootingcenter.com
713-984-9921
360tacticaltraining@gmail.com

Armiger Police Training Institute
Ken Murray
Gotha, Florida
www.armiger.net
407-532-7380
ken.murray@armiger.net

Agoge Training
John Brown
Montrose, Colorado
www.crossfitagoge.com
970-209-4222
John@crossfitagoge.com

Michael Bane
Downrange TV
www.downrange.tv
620-374-3079
office@downrange.tv

Steve Barron
Hocking College
Nelsonville, OH

Blacksheep Training
Kent O'Donnell
Farmington, NM

Blauer Tactical Systems
Tony Blauer
Virginia Beach, VA
tonyblauer.com
1-877-773-2748
combatives@blauertactical.com

Colorado Firearms Academy
Paul Hberstroh
Colorado
www.coloradofirearmsacademy.com
303-478-4712
training@ coloradofirearmsacademy.com

Defense Training International, Inc.
John S. Farnam
Laporte, CO
www.defense-training.com
970-482-0548
jsfarnam@aol.com

Direct Action Medical Network
Robert Smith, MD
Alexandria, LA
www.directactionmedicalnetwork.com
318-449-4467

Firearms Academy of Seattle, Inc.
Gila Hayes
Washington
www.firearmsacademy.com
360-978-6100

Tom Givens
Rangemaster
Memphis, TN
www.rangemaster.com
901-370-5600
rangemaster.tom@gmail.com

I.C.E. Training Company
Rob Pincus
Colorado
www.icetraining.us
info@icetraining.us
970-209-8092

Khyber Interactive Associates
Wes Doss
www.khybertraining.com
877-884-0909

Legal Defense Network, LLC
Marty Hayes
Onalaska, WA
www.armedcitizensnetwork.org
360-978-5200
info@ armedcitizensnetwork.org

LMS Training
John Chapman, Troy Price
Sparks, NV
lmsdefense.com
831.236.4690
Questions@LMSDefense.com

Martial Blade Concepts
Michael Janich
Longmont, CO
www.martialbladeconcepts.com
303-995-8848
info@martialbladeconcepts.com

Lt. Gary Meares (ret)
DGG Taser & Tactical Supply
Jacksonville, FL
www.dggtaser.com
866-626-8273
sales@dggtaser.com

New American Truth
Frank Borelli
Lusby, MD
www.newamericantruth.com
frank@newamericantruth.com

Options for Personal Security
Andy Stanford
www.opstraining.com
877-63-4677

Rogers Shooting School
Claude Werner
Ellijay, GA
www.rogers-shooting-school.com
904-642-7810

S.W.A.T. Magazine
Denny Hansen
www.swatmag.com
denny@swatmag.com

S2 Institute
Tim O'Rourke
Clearwater, FL
www.s2institute.com
727-461-0066
info@s2institute.com

Sabre Tactical Training, Resource and Research
Paul Castle
Nashville, TN
www.sabretactical.com
615-969-3377
pcastle@visi.net

Shivworks
Craig Douglas
www.shivworks.com

Shootrite Firearms Academy
Tiger Mckee
Langston, AL
www.shootrite.org
256-582-4777
tiger.mckee@shootrite.org

Randy Smith
Boalsburg, PA
www.pistoltraining.com
814-364-2303
rsmith637@aol.com

Dave Spaulding
Racstraining.com
Dspaulding1114@sbcglobal.net

Strategos International
Mark Warren & Vaughn Baker
Grandview, MO
www.strategosintl.com
888-569-5444
mark@strategosintl.com

Tactical Response
James Yeager
Camden, TN
www.tacticalresponse.com
1-877-7LETHAL
Info@TacticalResponse.com

Team One Network
John Meyer
Virginia
www.teamonenetwork.com
540-752-8190
john@teamonenetwork.com

Tony Scotti Associates
Tony Scotti
Medford, MA
www.securitydriver.com
781-395-3097
tonyscott@securitydriver.com

Thunder Ranch, Inc.
Clint Smith
Lakeview, OR
www.thunderranchinc.com
troregon@centurytel.net

INTEGRITY

CONSISTENCY

EFFICIENCY

Notes / Diagrams / Pictures

Date: | Course/Event:

Instructor: | Company/Agency:

Instr. Contact: | Total Hours:

Location/Host: | Certificate: Yes / No

Fee:

Topics:	Hours

Classmates & Contact Info:

Equipment Used/Purchased:

Instructor Comments & Signature:

Notes / Diagrams / Pictures

Date:	Course/Event:		
Instructor:		Company/Agency:	
Instr. Contact:			Total Hours:
Location/Host:			Certificate: Yes / No
			Fee:

Topics:	Hours

Classmates & Contact Info:

Equipment Used/Purchased:	Instructor Comments & Signature:

Notes / Diagrams / Pictures

Date:	Course/Event:	
Instructor:	Company/Agency:	
Instr. Contact:		Total Hours:
Location/Host:		Certificate: Yes / No
		Fee:

Topics:	Hours

Classmates & Contact Info:

Equipment Used/Purchased:	Instructor Comments & Signature:

Notes / Diagrams / Pictures

Date:	Course/Event:
Instructor:	Company/Agency:
Instr. Contact:	Total Hours:
Location/Host:	Certificate: Yes / No
	Fee:

Topics:	Hours

Classmates & Contact Info:

Equipment Used/Purchased:	Instructor Comments & Signature:

Notes / Diagrams / Pictures

Date:	Course/Event:

Instructor:	Company/Agency:

Instr. Contact:	Total Hours:
Location/Host:	Certificate: Yes / No
	Fee:

Topics:	Hours

Classmates & Contact Info:

Equipment Used/Purchased:	Instructor Comments & Signature:

Notes / Diagrams / Pictures

Date:	Course/Event:
Instructor:	Company/Agency:
Instr. Contact:	Total Hours:
Location/Host:	Certificate: Yes / No
	Fee:

Topics:	Hours

Classmates & Contact Info:

Equipment Used/Purchased:	Instructor Comments & Signature:

Notes / Diagrams / Pictures

Date:	Course/Event:

Instructor:	Company/Agency:

Instr. Contact:	Total Hours:
Location/Host:	Certificate: Yes / No
	Fee:

Topics:	Hours

Classmates & Contact Info:

Equipment Used/Purchased:	Instructor Comments & Signature:

Notes / Diagrams / Pictures

Date:	Course/Event:

Instructor:	Company/Agency:

Instr. Contact:	Total Hours:
Location/Host:	Certificate: Yes / No
	Fee:

Topics:	Hours

Classmates & Contact Info:

Equipment Used/Purchased:	Instructor Comments & Signature:

Notes / Diagrams / Pictures

Date:	Course/Event:
Instructor:	Company/Agency:
Instr. Contact:	Total Hours:
Location/Host:	Certificate: Yes / No
	Fee:

Topics:	Hours

Classmates & Contact Info:

Equipment Used/Purchased:	Instructor Comments & Signature:

Notes / Diagrams / Pictures

Date:	Course/Event:	
Instructor:	Company/Agency:	
Instr. Contact:		Total Hours:
Location/Host:		Certificate: Yes / No
		Fee:

Topics:	Hours

Classmates & Contact Info:

Equipment Used/Purchased:	Instructor Comments & Signature:

Notes / Diagrams / Pictures

Date:	Course/Event:		
Instructor:		Company/Agency:	
Instr. Contact:			Total Hours:
Location/Host:			Certificate: Yes / No
			Fee:

Topics:	Hours

Classmates & Contact Info:

Equipment Used/Purchased:	Instructor Comments & Signature:

Notes / Diagrams / Pictures

Date:	Course/Event:

Instructor:	Company/Agency:

Instr. Contact:	Total Hours:
Location/Host:	Certificate: Yes / No
	Fee:

Topics:	Hours

Classmates & Contact Info:

Equipment Used/Purchased:	Instructor Comments & Signature:

Notes / Diagrams / Pictures

Date:

Course/Event:

Instructor:

Company/Agency:

Instr. Contact:

Total Hours:

Location/Host:

Certificate: Yes / No

Fee:

Topics:	Hours

Classmates & Contact Info:

Equipment Used/Purchased:

Instructor Comments & Signature:

Notes / Diagrams / Pictures

Date:	Course/Event:

Instructor:	Company/Agency:

Instr. Contact:	Total Hours:
Location/Host:	Certificate: Yes / No
	Fee:

Topics:	Hours

Classmates & Contact Info:

Equipment Used/Purchased:	Instructor Comments & Signature:

Notes / Diagrams / Pictures

Date:	Course/Event:
Instructor:	Company/Agency:
Instr. Contact:	Total Hours:
Location/Host:	Certificate: Yes / No
	Fee:

Topics:	Hours

Classmates & Contact Info:

Equipment Used/Purchased:	Instructor Comments & Signature:

Notes / Diagrams / Pictures

Date:	Course/Event:

Instructor:	Company/Agency:

Instr. Contact:	Total Hours:
Location/Host:	Certificate: Yes / No
	Fee:

Topics:	Hours

Classmates & Contact Info:

Equipment Used/Purchased:	Instructor Comments & Signature:

Notes / Diagrams / Pictures

Date:	Course/Event:

Instructor:	Company/Agency:

Instr. Contact:	Total Hours:
Location/Host:	Certificate: Yes / No
	Fee:

Topics:	Hours

Classmates & Contact Info:

Equipment Used/Purchased:	Instructor Comments & Signature:

Notes / Diagrams / Pictures

Date:	Course/Event:

Instructor:	Company/Agency:

Instr. Contact:	Total Hours:
Location/Host:	Certificate: Yes / No
	Fee:

Topics:	Hours

Classmates & Contact Info:

Equipment Used/Purchased:	Instructor Comments & Signature:

Notes / Diagrams / Pictures

Date:	Course/Event:

Instructor:	Company/Agency:

Instr. Contact:	Total Hours:
Location/Host:	Certificate: Yes / No
	Fee:

Topics:	Hours

Classmates & Contact Info:

Equipment Used/Purchased:	Instructor Comments & Signature:

Notes / Diagrams / Pictures

Date:	Course/Event:
Instructor:	Company/Agency:
Instr. Contact:	Total Hours:
Location/Host:	Certificate: Yes / No
	Fee:

Topics:	Hours

Classmates & Contact Info:

Equipment Used/Purchased:	Instructor Comments & Signature:

Notes / Diagrams / Pictures

Date:	Course/Event:
Instructor:	Company/Agency:
Instr. Contact:	Total Hours:
Location/Host:	Certificate: Yes / No
	Fee:

Topics:	Hours

Classmates & Contact Info:

Equipment Used/Purchased:	Instructor Comments & Signature:

Notes / Diagrams / Pictures

Date:	Course/Event:
Instructor:	Company/Agency:
Instr. Contact:	Total Hours:
Location/Host:	Certificate: Yes / No
	Fee:

Topics:	Hours

Classmates & Contact Info:

Equipment Used/Purchased:	Instructor Comments & Signature:

Notes / Diagrams / Pictures

Date:	Course/Event:

Instructor:	Company/Agency:

Instr. Contact:	Total Hours:
Location/Host:	Certificate: Yes / No
	Fee:

Topics:	Hours

Classmates & Contact Info:

Equipment Used/Purchased:	Instructor Comments & Signature:

Notes / Diagrams / Pictures

Date:	Course/Event:
Instructor:	Company/Agency:
Instr. Contact:	Total Hours:
Location/Host:	Certificate: Yes / No
	Fee:

Topics:	Hours

Classmates & Contact Info:

Equipment Used/Purchased:	Instructor Comments & Signature:

Notes / Diagrams / Pictures

Date:	Course/Event:
Instructor:	Company/Agency:
Instr. Contact:	Total Hours:
Location/Host:	Certificate: Yes / No
	Fee:

Topics:	Hours

Classmates & Contact Info:

Equipment Used/Purchased:	Instructor Comments & Signature:

Notes / Diagrams / Pictures

Date:	Course/Event:
Instructor:	Company/Agency:
Instr. Contact:	Total Hours:
Location/Host:	Certificate: Yes / No
	Fee:

Topics:	Hours

Classmates & Contact Info:

Equipment Used/Purchased:	Instructor Comments & Signature:

Notes / Diagrams / Pictures

Date:	Course/Event:
Instructor:	Company/Agency:
Instr. Contact:	Total Hours:
Location/Host:	Certificate: Yes / No
	Fee:

Topics:	Hours

Classmates & Contact Info:

Equipment Used/Purchased:	Instructor Comments & Signature:

Notes / Diagrams / Pictures

Date:	Course/Event:
Instructor:	Company/Agency:
Instr. Contact:	Total Hours:
Location/Host:	Certificate: Yes / No
	Fee:

Topics:	Hours

Classmates & Contact Info:

Equipment Used/Purchased:	Instructor Comments & Signature:

Notes / Diagrams / Pictures

Date:	Course/Event:		
Instructor:		Company/Agency:	
Instr. Contact:			Total Hours:
Location/Host:			Certificate: Yes / No
			Fee:

Topics:	Hours

Classmates & Contact Info:

Equipment Used/Purchased:	Instructor Comments & Signature:

Notes / Diagrams / Pictures

Date:	Course/Event:

Instructor:	Company/Agency:

Instr. Contact:	Total Hours:
Location/Host:	Certificate: Yes / No
	Fee:

Topics:	Hours

Classmates & Contact Info:

Equipment Used/Purchased:	Instructor Comments & Signature:

Notes / Diagrams / Pictures

Date:	Course/Event:
Instructor:	Company/Agency:
Instr. Contact:	Total Hours:
Location/Host:	Certificate: Yes / No
	Fee:

Topics:	Hours

Classmates & Contact Info:

Equipment Used/Purchased:	Instructor Comments & Signature:

Notes / Diagrams / Pictures

Date:	Course/Event:
Instructor:	Company/Agency:
Instr. Contact:	Total Hours:
Location/Host:	Certificate: Yes / No
	Fee:

Topics:	Hours

Classmates & Contact Info:

Equipment Used/Purchased:	Instructor Comments & Signature:

Notes / Diagrams / Pictures

Date:	Course/Event:
Instructor:	Company/Agency:
Instr. Contact:	Total Hours:
Location/Host:	Certificate: Yes / No
	Fee:

Topics:	Hours

Classmates & Contact Info:

Equipment Used/Purchased:	Instructor Comments & Signature:

Notes / Diagrams / Pictures

Date:	Course/Event:
Instructor:	Company/Agency:
Instr. Contact:	Total Hours:
Location/Host:	Certificate: Yes / No
	Fee:

Topics:	Hours

Classmates & Contact Info:

Equipment Used/Purchased:	Instructor Comments & Signature:

Notes / Diagrams / Pictures

Date:	Course/Event:		
Instructor:		Company/Agency:	
Instr. Contact:			Total Hours:
Location/Host:			Certificate: Yes / No
			Fee:

Topics:	Hours

Classmates & Contact Info:

Equipment Used/Purchased:	Instructor Comments & Signature:

Notes / Diagrams / Pictures

Date:	Course/Event:

Instructor:	Company/Agency:

Instr. Contact:	Total Hours:
Location/Host:	Certificate: Yes / No
	Fee:

Topics:	Hours

Classmates & Contact Info:

Equipment Used/Purchased:	Instructor Comments & Signature:

Notes / Diagrams / Pictures

Date:	Course/Event:

Instructor:	Company/Agency:

Instr. Contact:	Total Hours:
Location/Host:	Certificate: Yes / No
	Fee:

Topics:	Hours

Classmates & Contact Info:

Equipment Used/Purchased:	Instructor Comments & Signature:

Notes / Diagrams / Pictures

Date:	Course/Event:
Instructor:	Company/Agency:
Instr. Contact:	Total Hours:
Location/Host:	Certificate: Yes / No
	Fee:

Topics:	Hours

Classmates & Contact Info:

Equipment Used/Purchased:	Instructor Comments & Signature:

Notes / Diagrams / Pictures

Date:	Course/Event:
Instructor:	Company/Agency:
Instr. Contact:	Total Hours:
Location/Host:	Certificate: Yes / No
	Fee:

Topics:	Hours

Classmates & Contact Info:

Equipment Used/Purchased:	Instructor Comments & Signature:

Notes / Diagrams / Pictures

Date:	Course/Event:

Instructor:	Company/Agency:

Instr. Contact:	Total Hours:
Location/Host:	Certificate: Yes / No
	Fee:

Topics:	Hours

Classmates & Contact Info:

Equipment Used/Purchased:	Instructor Comments & Signature:

Notes / Diagrams / Pictures

Date: | Course/Event:

Instructor: | Company/Agency:

Instr. Contact: | Total Hours:

Location/Host: | Certificate: Yes / No

Fee:

Topics:	Hours

Classmates & Contact Info:

Equipment Used/Purchased:

Instructor Comments & Signature:

Notes / Diagrams / Pictures

Date:	Course/Event:

Instructor:	Company/Agency:

Instr. Contact:	Total Hours:
Location/Host:	Certificate: Yes / No
	Fee:

Topics:	Hours

Classmates & Contact Info:

Equipment Used/Purchased:	Instructor Comments & Signature:

Notes / Diagrams / Pictures

Date:	Course/Event:

Instructor:	Company/Agency:

Instr. Contact:	Total Hours:
Location/Host:	Certificate: Yes / No
	Fee:

Topics:	Hours

Classmates & Contact Info:

Equipment Used/Purchased:	Instructor Comments & Signature:

Notes / Diagrams / Pictures

Date:	Course/Event:

Instructor:	Company/Agency:

Instr. Contact:	Total Hours:
Location/Host:	Certificate: Yes / No
	Fee:

Topics:	Hours

Classmates & Contact Info:

Equipment Used/Purchased:	Instructor Comments & Signature:

Notes / Diagrams / Pictures

Date:	Course/Event:

Instructor:	Company/Agency:

Instr. Contact:	Total Hours:
Location/Host:	Certificate: Yes / No
	Fee:

Topics:	Hours

Classmates & Contact Info:

Equipment Used/Purchased:	Instructor Comments & Signature:

Notes / Diagrams / Pictures

Date:	Course/Event:

Instructor:	Company/Agency:

Instr. Contact:	Total Hours:
Location/Host:	Certificate: Yes / No
	Fee:

Topics:	Hours

Classmates & Contact Info:

Equipment Used/Purchased:	Instructor Comments & Signature:

Notes / Diagrams / Pictures

Date:	Course/Event:
Instructor:	Company/Agency:
Instr. Contact:	Total Hours:
Location/Host:	Certificate: Yes / No
	Fee:

Topics:	Hours

Classmates & Contact Info:

Equipment Used/Purchased:	Instructor Comments & Signature:

Notes / Diagrams / Pictures

Date:	Course/Event:

Instructor:	Company/Agency:

Instr. Contact:	Total Hours:
Location/Host:	Certificate: Yes / No
	Fee:

Topics:	Hours

Classmates & Contact Info:

Equipment Used/Purchased:	Instructor Comments & Signature:

Notes / Diagrams / Pictures

Date:	Course/Event:

Instructor:	Company/Agency:

Instr. Contact:	Total Hours:
Location/Host:	Certificate: Yes / No
	Fee:

Topics:	Hours

Classmates & Contact Info:

Equipment Used/Purchased:	Instructor Comments & Signature:

Notes / Diagrams / Pictures

Date:	Course/Event:

Instructor:	Company/Agency:

Instr. Contact:	Total Hours:
Location/Host:	Certificate: Yes / No
	Fee:

Topics:	Hours

Classmates & Contact Info:

Equipment Used/Purchased:	Instructor Comments & Signature:

Notes / Diagrams / Pictures

Date:	Course/Event:		
Instructor:		Company/Agency:	
Instr. Contact:			Total Hours:
Location/Host:			Certificate: Yes / No
			Fee:

Topics:	Hours

Classmates & Contact Info:

Equipment Used/Purchased:	Instructor Comments & Signature:

Notes / Diagrams / Pictures

Date:	Course/Event:

Instructor:	Company/Agency:

Instr. Contact:	Total Hours:
Location/Host:	Certificate: Yes / No
	Fee:

Topics:	Hours

Classmates & Contact Info:

Equipment Used/Purchased:	Instructor Comments & Signature:

Notes / Diagrams / Pictures

Date:	Course/Event:

Instructor:	Company/Agency:

Instr. Contact:	Total Hours:
Location/Host:	Certificate: Yes / No
	Fee:

Topics:	Hours

Classmates & Contact Info:

Equipment Used/Purchased:	Instructor Comments & Signature:

Notes / Diagrams / Pictures

Date:	Course/Event:

Instructor:	Company/Agency:

Instr. Contact:	Total Hours:
Location/Host:	Certificate: Yes / No
	Fee:

Topics:	Hours

Classmates & Contact Info:

Equipment Used/Purchased:	Instructor Comments & Signature:

Notes / Diagrams / Pictures

Date:	Course/Event:

Instructor:	Company/Agency:

Instr. Contact:	Total Hours:
Location/Host:	Certificate: Yes / No
	Fee:

Topics:	Hours

Classmates & Contact Info:

Equipment Used/Purchased:	Instructor Comments & Signature:

When you've filled these pages, look for

The

Training Log Book II

With space to record over 100 additional training Events!

Available in 2009!